Pokémon ADVENTURES
Emerald
Volume 26
Perfect Square Edition

Story by HIDENORI KUSAKA
Art by SATOSHI YAMAMOTO

© 2015 Pokémon.
© 1995–2015 Nintendo/Creatures Inc./GAME FREAK inc.
TM, ®, and character names are trademarks of Nintendo.
POCKET MONSTERS SPECIAL Vol. 26
by Hidenori KUSAKA, Satoshi YAMAMOTO
© 1997 Hidenori KUSAKA, Satoshi YAMAMOTO
All rights reserved.
Original Japanese edition published by SHOGAKUKAN.
English translation rights in the United States of America,
Canada, the United Kingdom, Ireland, Australia and
New Zealand arranged with SHOGAKUKAN.

English Adaptation/Bryant Turnage
Translation/Tetsuichiro Miyaki
Touch-up & Lettering/Annaliese Christman
Design/Shawn Carrico
Editor/Annette Roman

Printed in the U.S.A.

Published by VIZ Media, LLC
P.O. Box 77010
San Francisco, CA 94107

10 9 8 7 6 5 4 3 2 1
First printing, January 2015

SPECIAL OBJECT

The Pokédex holders and their stories

Kanto region

Yellow

Red

Green

Blue

1st Chapter

Red, a young boy from Pallet Town, receives a Pokédex from Professor Oak and heads out on a Pokémon training journey. Along the way, he meets two other Trainers, Blue, who becomes his rival, and Green. Red fights evil Team Rocket with his new friends and then becomes Champion of the Pokémon League.

2nd Chapter

Two years later, Red suddenly disappears and Yellow, a mysterious new Trainer, appears at Professor Oak's laboratory in search of him.

Professor Oak

Pokémon
ADVENTURES
EMERALD

Story by
Hidenori Kusaka

Art by
Satoshi Yamamoto

26
VOLUME TWENTY-SIX

POKÉMON

Gold

Crystal

Silver

4th Chapter

Pokémon Trainer Ruby has a passion for Pokémon Contests. He runs away from home right after his family moves to Littleroot Town. He meets a wild girl named Sapphire and they pledge to compete with each other in an 80-day challenge to...

3rd Chapter

A year later, Gold, a boy living in New Bark Town in a house full of Pokémon, sets out on a journey in pursuit of Silver, a Trainer who stole a Totodile from Professor Elm's laboratory. The two don't get along at first, but eventually they become partners fighting side by side. During their journey, they meet Crystal, the trainer who Professor Elm entrusts with the completion of his Pokédex. Together, the trio succeed to shatter the evil scheme of the Mask of Ice, a villain who leads what remains of Team Rocket.

Standing in Yellow's way is the Kanto Elite Four, led by Lance. In a major battle at Cerise Island, Yellow manages to stymie the group's evil ambitions.

Professor Birch

Professor Elm

Red

Green

Blue

Kanto region

Sapphire

Ruby

Six months later, a new adventure unfolds for Red and his friends on the Sevii Islands. After a deadly battle, Red manages to defeat Deoxys, who has fallen into the hands of Giovanni. Silver, in search of his true identity, is faced with the shocking truth that Giovanni is his father. Red and his friends manage to safely land the Team Rocket airship, which was flying out of control thanks to Carr, one of the Three Beasts, who betrayed Team Rocket. But then another of the Three Beasts, Sird, appears, and in a mysterious flash of light the five Pokédex holders—Red, Blue, Green, Yellow and Silver—are petrified. Literally!

5th Chapter

...win every Pokémon Contest and every Pokémon Gym Battle, respectively. Meanwhile, in the Hoenn region, Team Aqua and Team Magma set their evil plot in motion. As a result, Legendary Pokémon Groudon and Kyogre are awakened and inflict catastrophic climate changes on Hoenn. In the end, thanks to Ruby and Sapphire's heroic efforts, the two legendary Pokémon go back into hibernation.

POKÉMON

ADVENTURES

EMERALD

26
VOLUME TWENTY-SIX

CONTENTS

◆Emerald

The Sixth Chapter

◆303◆
Never Spritz a Knotty Sudowoodo

OH, REALLY? WAS THE STONE PLATE HELPFUL?

THESE THREE POKÉMON USED UP ALL THEIR STRENGTH DURING THE KYOGRE-GROUDON CRISIS. THEY'VE BEEN WANDERING AROUND EVER SINCE.

HELLO? IT'S ME.

I GOT 'EM!

KLTTR

KLTTR

...BUT I WOULDN'T HAVE BEEN ABLE TO CAPTURE THEM WITHOUT IT!

IT WAS. TO BE HONEST, I WASN'T SURE WHAT I WAS SUPPOSED TO MAKE OF THIS GLUED-TOGETHER PLATE...

AND... I CAN USE THESE THREE, RIGHT?

YEAH, GO AHEAD.

HEH! I'M JUST TENACIOUS!

ONLY A SNEAKY GUY LIKE YOU COULD MANAGE TO GATHER ALL THOSE SHATTERED FRAGMENTS TO RECREATE THIS STONE PLATE.

12

♦ 303 ♦ ⠒⠂⠶⠄⠲⠂⠴⠂⠛
⠂⠒

IT'S THE NEWEST POKÉMON BATTLE TREND, IN WHICH CHALLENGERS MUST FACE A VARIETY OF GAMES AT SEVEN FACILITIES!

KABAM

KRKK

POOM

KRKK

OOOH, THE DAY HAS FINALLY COME!

IT'S MEDIA WEEK'S SPOTLIGHT ON...THE BATTLE FRONTIER!

I HOPE I RUN INTO A CHALLENGER SO I CAN GET IN AN INTERVIEW BEFORE THE BATTLES BEGIN—

I'VE GOT SOME TIME TO KILL... GUESS I'LL TAKE A LOOK-SEE AROUND THE PLACE. IT'S HUGE...

GG LLUBB

...THIS AFTERNOON AT 1:00 P.M.!

THE OPENING CEREMONY, INCLUDING AN EXCLUSIVE PRESS INTERVIEW WITH THE OWNER, SCOTT, BEGINS...

BATTLE FRONTIER

KA FUID

IT WOULD BE A SHAME TO JUST TOSS IT. I'LL USE IT TO WATER THIS TREE...

SPLASH

OOF. I SHOULDN'T HAVE BOUGHT SUCH A LARGE BOTTLE. I CAN'T FINISH IT.

Fresh Water

IT BELONGS TO SOMEONE NAMED...

ENTRY NAME
EMERALD
042-9187-6342-00135

...EMERALD.

OH! THIS IS...

...A FRONTIER PASS!

HUH ?!

I WONDER WHERE IT CAME FROM...

..."WHAT DO YOU LIKE MOST ABOUT POKÉMON?"

SO I CAN'T ANSWER YOUR QUESTION...

THAT'S RIGHT!

YOU DON'T HAVE A **SINGLE** POKÉMON WITH YOU?!

WFF

WFF

YOU'VE COME TO THE BATTLE FRONTIER BECAUSE YOU LOVE POKÉMON, HAVEN'T YOU? HECK, **EVERYONE** LOVES POKÉMON!

BUT YOU MUST BE A POKÉMON **TRAINER**, RIGHT?!

YOU DON'T GET IT, DO YOU?

SHNK

SHING

TO THE PRESS...

Thank you so much for attending this press conference at the Battle Frontier today. I've spent a fortune creating this facility to offer Trainers the opportunity to participate in cutting-edge Pokémon Battles. We offer a variety of styles of battle at our facilities. Enjoy!

OWNER: SCOTT

■ PRE-OPENING EVENT ■ FOR THE PRESS

The pre-opening Media Week starts tomorrow. The Battle Frontier will officially open to the public the following week.

■ LOCATION/ TRANSPORTATION ■

The Battle Frontier is located on an island in the Hoenn region, in between Pacifidlog Town and Ever Grande City. Enjoy a pleasant cruise there via ferry departing from Slateport City or Lilycove City.

ROUTE FROM LILYCOVE CITY

ROUTE FROM SLATE- PORT CITY

Swanky Showdown
with Swalot

POKÉMON ADVENTURES·THE SIXTH CHAPTER·EMERALD

YOU ASKED ME FOR HELP!

SO I HELPED YOU!

...THAT VIOLENT POKÉMON INSTANTLY CALMED DOWN.

...ON THE GROUND AND...

EMER-ALD "SHOT" A WEIRD PAT-TERN...

TAKE IT EASY... EASY...

PAT

FWUMP

DID YOU POUR WATER ON THIS SUDOWOODO... THINKING IT WAS A TREE OR SOMETHING?

HEY! I THINK THIS IS ALL YOUR FAULT!

No.185 SUDOWOODO
Imitation Pokémon

Height: 3'11"
Weight: 83.8 lbs.

It mimics a tree to avoid being attacked by enemies. But since its forelegs remain green throughout the year, it is easily identified as a fake in the winter.

SUDO-WOODO...

...DOESN'T LIKE WATER.

AREA | CRY | SIZE | QUIT

SEE...?

RSTL

JUST GOES TO SHOW, YOU SHOULDN'T JUDGE A BOOK BY ITS COVER!

AND JUST BECAUSE I'M A KID, THAT DOESN'T MEAN I CAN'T MAKE IT THROUGH THE BATTLE FRONTIER...

AAAAGGH! I TOTALLY FORGOT ABOUT THE BATTLE FRONTIER!

OH...

WHAT WAS **THAT** ALL ABOUT?

WOW...

RSTL

HE MANAGED TO CALM THAT SUDOWOODO DOWN QUICKLY THOUGH. HE APPEARS TO KNOW A LOT ABOUT POKÉMON.

HE DOESN'T LIKE POKÉMON, BUT...HE LIKES POKÉMON BATTLES?!

EMERALD IS CERTAINLY...

...A STRANGE BOY...

AND... HE ALLOWED SUDOWOODO TO RETURN TO THE WILD. HE DIDN'T EVEN CONSIDER CAPTURING IT.

SEEMS HE WAS TELLING THE TRUTH WHEN HE SAID HE DOESN'T HAVE ANY POKÉMON.

KRMBL

HMM... THEY'VE GOT SOME SORT OF STRINGS ATTACHED TO THEM.

THESE ARE FAR TOO FRAGILE TO HURT ANYONE.

THOSE "BULLETS" HE SHOT INTO THE GROUND... NOW THAT I TAKE A GOOD LOOK AT THEM, I SEE THEY'RE JUST LUMPS OF MUD.

... CALMING PELLET.

THEY MUST BE SOME SORT OF...

OH NO!

AND NOW FOR THE OPENING CEREMONY OF THE BATTLE FRONTIER...

AND MR. SCOTT'S PRESS CONFERENCE IS ABOUT TO START!

MEMBERS OF THE PRESS...

I FORGOT TO FIND SUBJECTS TO INTERVIEW!

HEY, YOU!

I NEED TO REGISTER AT THE FRONT DESK, BUT I CAN'T FIND IT!

IS IT THIS WAY?

THAT WAY?

OR THIS WAY?

HUH?

WSSSPF

HUH?! WHO ARE YOU?!

WHICH WAY DO I GO TO GET TO THE REGISTRATION DESK?!

GRAB

GIMME A RIDE!

GET OFF!

GIMME A RIDE!

GET OFF!

OH, YOU MUST BE ONE OF THE STAFF! PERFECT! GIMME A LIFT TO THE FRONT DESK, WILL YOU?

ARE YOU KIDDING?! GET OFF!

THIS CORRIDOR IS OFF-LIMITS TO OUTSIDERS! HOW'D YOU GET IN HERE?!

38

I'M SCOTT, THE OWNER OF THIS BATTLE ARENA!

DID YOU ENJOY THE THRILLING BATTLE DEMONSTRATION?! I APOLOGIZE FOR KEEPING YOU WAITING...

AND THOSE SEVEN ARENAS ARE...

IT'S A POKÉMON TRAINER'S DREAM, A PLACE WHERE THEY CAN ENJOY SEVEN DIFFERENT TYPES OF BATTLES!

THE BATTLE FRONTIER IS ON THE CUTTING EDGE OF POKÉMON BATTLES!

THE BATTLE DOME, WHICH TESTS YOUR TACTICS!

THE BATTLE PALACE, WHICH TESTS YOUR SPIRIT!

THE BATTLE ARENA, WHICH TESTS YOUR GUTS!

THE BATTLE TOWER, WHICH TESTS YOUR ABILITY!

THE BATTLE PYRAMID, WHICH TESTS YOUR COURAGE!

THE BATTLE PIKE, WHICH TESTS YOUR LUCK!

THE BATTLE FACTORY, WHICH TESTS YOUR KNOWLEDGE!

YOU'VE ALREADY MET TWO OF THEM DURING THE BATTLE DEMONSTRATION...

RMBL RMBL

NOW ALLOW ME TO INTRODUCE YOU TO THE TRAINERS WHO AWAIT CHALLENGERS AT THE END OF EACH ARENA...

SHNK

ME?

WHO... ARE YOU?!

HUH?!

OW...

POP

I'M EMERALD.

MY NAME'S EMERALD!

POKÉMON BATTLES' NUMBER-ONE FAN, EMERALD!

I'M HERE TO CHALLENGE THE BATTLE FRONTIER!

NO. WE'RE HAVING A PRESS CONFERENCE IN THIS HALL, AND I'M SCOTT, THE OWNER OF THE BATTLE FRONTIER!

AND WHAT HAVE YOU DONE WITH TUCKER?!

...CE TO MEET YOU, TYLER.

IS THIS THE FRONT DESK? ARE YOU IN CHARGE OF REGISTERING TRAINERS?

DEAR MEMBERS OF THE PRESS...

Thank you so much for coming to my
Battle Frontier today. Allow me to take
this opportunity to explain the rules for
Pokémon Battles here...

■ LIMITED POKÉMON ■ USAGE

You may not enter two of the same
Pokémon into a battle.
*Prior permission must be obtained to
participate with an Egg or Legendary
Pokémon.
*Your challenge might not be accepted.
*On the other hand, there is a possibility
that our Frontier Brains will use **your**
Pokémon in battle.

■ ITEM USAGE ■

Apart from certain exceptions, Trainers
are not allowed to use items during
challenges. But Pokémon may hold
an item before battle.

■ NUMBER OF MOVES PERMITTED ■

Each Pokémon is only allowed four moves during a
battle. These moves must be registered before the
battle. No other moves are permitted.

◆ ∃05 ◆

Interesting Interactions
Involving Illumise

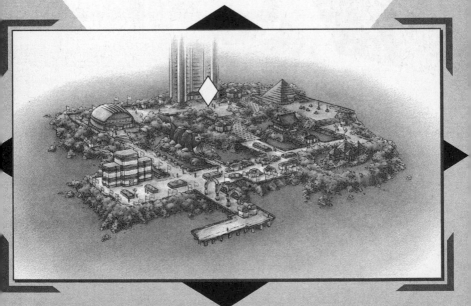

ᴏKÉMON ADVENTURES•THE SIXTH CHAPTER•EMERALD

AIIYEE! YOU LITTLE BRAT!

PSTL

I FINALLY FOUND TUCKER!

PHEW.

ZIP

NOW THEN, WHAT SHOULD WE DO WITH YOU?!

AND I GOT ME AN OFFICIAL FRONTIER PASS! SEE?!

JUST BECAUSE YOU'VE GOT A FRONTIER PASS DOESN'T MEAN YOU CAN DO AS YOU LIKE.

WE **HEARD** YOU, LOUD-MOUTH.

GRAB

LEMME CHALLENGE THE BATTLE FRONTIER!!

SO LEMME FIGHT! LEMME FIGHT!

WHOA!

SPROING

THAT'S **MY** PASS! WHAT'D YOU DO THAT FOR?! GIVE IT BACK!

LUNGE

QUICK ATTACK!

BUT HE'S BECOME A MEDIA SENSATION!

HUH?

I'LL SAY. ARE YOU AWARE THAT YOU JUST RUINED THE OPENING CEREMONY AND PRESS CONFERENCE?

HE CERTAINLY IS FULL OF SURPRISES...

THIS JUST IN— THE BATTLE FRONTIER, A NEW POKÉMON BATTLE FACILITY, WAS OPENED TO THE PRESS TODAY.

AND NOW FOR THE 6 O'CLOCK NEWS...

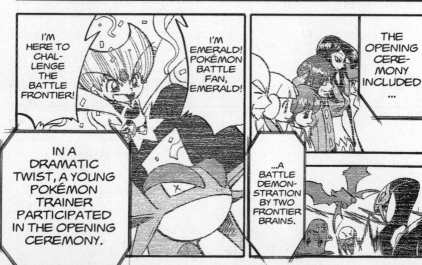

I'M HERE TO CHALLENGE THE BATTLE FRONTIER!

I'M EMERALD! POKÉMON BATTLE FAN, EMERALD!

THE OPENING CERE- MONY INCLUDED ...

IN A DRAMATIC TWIST, A YOUNG POKÉMON TRAINER PARTICIPATED IN THE OPENING CEREMONY.

...A BATTLE DEMON- STRATION BY TWO FRONTIER BRAINS.

ME TOO!

I CAN'T WAIT TO HEAR HOW THAT BOY DOES AT THE BATTLE FRONTIER!

Hey, I look great on TV!

THEY SEEM TO HAVE MADE A MISTAKE...

HE ANNOUNCED HIS CHALLENGE IN SUCH A PUBLIC, GRAND GESTURE...

THE PRESS WILL MAKE A FUSS IF WE DON'T ALLOW HIM TO TAKE PART.

I SEE NO REASON WHY WE SHOULDN'T REVOKE HIS FRONTIER PASS TO PREVENT THIS BOOR FROM PAR-TICIPATING.

HOW-EVER...

WHAT SHOULD WE DO, MR. SCOTT? MANNERS AND PROTOCOL ARE VERY IMPORTANT FOR A TRAINER CHALLENGING THE BATTLE FRONTIER.

...I DETEST IGNORANCE. AND HE DOESN'T APPEAR TO HAVE A SPECK OF KNOWLEDGE INSIDE THAT BIG HEAD OF HIS!

I WON'T ALLOW HIM TO RIDICULE THE BATTLE FRONTIER AND MAKE A FOOL OUT OF US FRONTIER BRAINS.

DRAG

BE-SIDES...

WHOA!

TOSS

OH WOW...!

SNEAK

PREPARE TO BATTLE FACTORY HEAD NOLAND!

I AM THE FACTORY HEAD! MY NAME IS NOLAND!

HEY, EMER-ALD!

FJ MP

GRRRR
...

PHEW! HE'S ALL RIGHT ...

THAT'S WHAT'S BOTHERING HIM?

TINK

THAT STUPID COBBLER! THESE SHOES FALL APART SO EASILY!

TIN...

IT IS **NOT** OKAY! WE'RE TALKING ABOUT THE **FRONTIER BRAINS**— THE STRONGEST POKÉMON TRAINERS HERE!

EMERALD! WHAT ARE YOU GOING TO DO NOW?!

THE FRONTIER BRAINS ARE SERIOUS! YOU MADE FUN OF THEM, AND NOW THEY'RE MAD!

ROLL

OW ...

THEY'RE ALL PREPARED TO FIGHT YOU WITH ALL THEIR MIGHT...

WILL YOU LISTEN TO ME ...?!

IT'S OKAY. DON'T WORRY ABOUT IT.

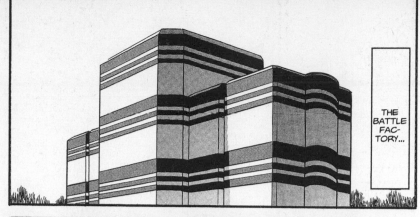

THE BATTLE FACTORY...

THE BOY WHO APPEARED DURING THE OPENING CEREMONY WILL BE FACING THE FRONTIER BRAINS TODAY!

PERFECT. THIS WILL HELP US LEARN MORE ABOUT THE RULES OF BATTLE IN EACH OF THE FACILITIES.

WHAT A CLEVER WAY TO PRESENT THIS NEW BATTLE-GROUND!

THE FIRST LOCATION IS THE BATTLE FACTORY. I WONDER WHAT KIND OF BATTLE THEY FIGHT IN...

SSHH! IT'S TIME.

THANK YOU FOR COMING HERE SO EARLY IN THE MORNING. MY NAME IS NOLAND, AND I AM IN CHARGE OF THIS ARENA.

MY TRAINER CLASS IS FACTORY HEAD. YOU MAY ADDRESS ME AS FACTORY HEAD NOLAND.

SINGLE BATTLE OR DOUBLE BATTLE?

SIN-GLE!

FIFTY!

AND THE LEVEL?

EMER-ALD!

...CHOOSE YOUR RENTAL POKÉMON.

RMMRMMRMM

NOW YOU MAY...

YOU MAY CHOOSE THREE POKÉMON TO USE IN BATTLE.

THAT'S RIGHT. YOU DON'T USE YOUR OWN POKÉMON ...

...WHEN YOU CHALLENGE THIS FACILITY.

RENTAL POKÉMON?!

HMM ...

I DON'T HAVE A FIXED TEAM OF POKÉMON EITHER.

SO I'LL CHOOSE THREE RENTAL POKÉ-MON TO FIGHT WITH AS WELL.

THE ITEMS THEY'RE HOLD-ING...

I NEED TO CHECK THEIR MOVES, THEIR ATTACK AND DEFENSE STYLES...

2

Rhyhorn ♂
Item
Leftovers

3

Ludicolo ♂
Item
Scope Lens

1

Skarmory ♂
Item
Quick Claw

OKAY! I CHOOSE THESE THREE!

TING

RAAAH

BATTLE ...

LET THE BATTLE BEGIN!

VOOP

...START!

RIGHT NOW, HE'S FIGHTING A VIRTUAL TRAINER CREATED BY THE COMPUTER. MY POKÉMON WILL TAKE ORDERS FROM THAT VIRTUAL TRAINER DURING THIS BATTLE.

FIRST, I NEED TO DETERMINE IF A CHALLENGER IS WORTHY OF ME.

DID YOU REALLY THINK YOU'D GET TO FIGHT ME RIGHT AWAY?

WHAT?! YOU'RE NOT GOING TO FIGHT HIM, NOLAND?!

SEVEN BATTLES MAKE UP ONE SET IN THIS FACILITY.

HE WILL FACE ME IN THE SEVENTH BATTLE OF THE SIXTH SET.

BUT OF COURSE...

...THE CHALLENGE WILL END THE MOMENT HE'S DEFEATED!

R MB L R MB

I WAS THINKING ABOUT USING A FLYING-TYPE MOVE TO DEFEAT IT QUICKLY!

SHOOT! MY POKÉMON GOT HIT WITH CONFUSION!

FLATTER!

ZOOP! ZOOP!

SMASH

ROCK SLIDE!

OH WELL! CHANGE OF PLANS!

PHEW.

THE POKÉMON HAVE FAINTED... ALL THREE OF THEM ARE DOWN! THE BATTLE IS OVER!

VOOP

YOU HAVE TO WIN FORTY-ONE BATTLES IN A ROW BEFORE YOU CAN EVEN FACE THE FRONTIER BRAIN!

S-SEVEN OF THESE MAKE UP ONE BATTLE SET. AND EMERALD CAN ONLY FIGHT NOLAND AT THE END OF THE SIXTH SET. THAT MEANS...

RMMR MM

OF COURSE.

CATCH

I'M ALLOWED TO HEAL MY POKÉMON AFTER EACH BATTLE, RIGHT?

THAT'S RIGHT. AND WHAT MAKES THIS EVEN HARDER IS THAT...

YOU WOULD PROBABLY HAVE SELF-DESTRUCTED THANKS TO CONFUSION IF YOU'D GOTTEN HUNG UP ON DEFEATING ILLUMISE USING SKARMORY'S FLYING-TYPE MOVE.

THAT WAS A GOOD DECISION.

NOW DO YOU UNDERSTAND HOW DIFFICULT THIS BATTLEGROUND IS?

YOU HAVE TO USE RENTAL POKÉMON YOU JUST MET FOR THE FIRST TIME.

...YOU'RE NOT ALLOWED TO USE YOUR OWN POKÉMON.

THAT'S WHY, AT THE BATTLE FACTORY, YOU HAVE TO HAVE A DEEP KNOWLEDGE OF POKÉMON, THEIR TYPES, MOVES AND ABILITIES!

AND THE OTHER IMPORTANT FEATURE OF THE BATTLES HERE IS...

...TRADING.

KNOWLEDGE RULES!

...AND TRADE IT FOR ONE OF THE THREE POKÉMON YOU JUST FOUGHT.

YOU CAN LET GO OF ONE OF THE POKÉMON IN YOUR GROUP...

...YOU HAVE THE OPTION TO TRADE YOUR POKÉMON.

CHALLENGER...

OKAY... I'LL LET GO OF SKARMORY THEN.

AND I WANT ILLUMISE IN EXCHANGE.

BLIP

2

3

TO CONTINUE FIGHTING, YOU NEED TO KEEP CHANGING UP THE POKÉMON ON YOUR TEAM—AND THAT'S THE **BATTLE FACTORY**!

YOU USE RENTAL POKÉMON TO FIGHT, AND YOU HAD BETTER PAY ATTENTION TO YOUR OPPONENT'S POKÉMON AS WELL. BECAUSE YOUR OPPONENT MIGHT HAVE A POKÉMON YOU WANT THAT YOU CAN ADD TO YOUR GROUP LATER BY TRADING.

VOOP

SECOND BATTLE... BEGIN!

DEAR MEMBERS OF THE PRESS...

Thank you for visiting my Battle Frontier today. Permit me to continue explaining the rules of this facility...

OWNER: SCOTT

■ FOR CONVENIENCE, WE USE ■ NUMBERS TO REPRESENT A POKÉMON'S STRENGTH.

To ensure a fair battle, we represent the strengths of our Pokémon with numbers we call "levels." Challengers may use their PokéNav to check the level of their Pokémon before a battle.

CHALLENGERS MAY CHOOSE BETWEEN LEVEL 50 AND OPEN LEVEL.

You may choose between two courses. In the "Level 50" course, the highest level for your Pokémon is 50. But the "Open Level" course has no Pokémon level limits.

■ FUNCTIONS OF THE ■ FRONTIER PASS

A Frontier Pass is handed out to challengers. This pass has many features, such as a map to check where each facility is located. Battle records are also recorded on the Frontier Pass. You may record any battle you wish and replay it later.

Pinsir Me,
I Must Be Dreaming

SLAKING, SLACK OFF!

LET'S HEAL THE DAMAGE!

OWW... THAT WAS A PRETTY PAINFUL ATTACK.

AND ONCE YOUR DAMAGE IS HEALED ...

...FEINT ATTACK!

...AND SWAP IT WITH THE LINOONE ON MY OPPONENT'S TEAM!

I'LL LET GO OF SLAKING...

OKAY, I'M GONNA TRADE AGAIN!

GOOD! HE GOT THE MESSAGE!

OH, SHOOT!

WHAT?! YOU'RE GOING TO LET GO OF THAT POWERFUL SLAKING?! DON'T DO IT, EMERALD!

70

AND A CHANCE TO TAKE A REGULAR BREAK... NICE VIEW!

'SCUSE ME— BATHROOM BREAK!

MISTAKES?!

I'M WORRIED ABOUT YOU... YOU'VE BEEN FIGHTING FOR SO LONG, YOU'RE STARTING TO MAKE MISTAKES!

DON'T JUMP!!

YOUR BATTLE ISN'T GOING THAT BADLY!

Huh'?

YEAH? AND...?

I'M NO EXPERT TRAINER, BUT I AM A JOURNALIST. I OBSERVE AND ANALYZE.

TOILET

THAT'S RIGHT.

I'VE WATCHED A LOT OF BATTLES IN MY TIME...

THAT'S RIGHT!

SO...YOU THINK I'M MAKING MISTAKES IN MY BATTLES... THAT I'M CHOOSING THE WRONG POKÉMON MAYBE?

PLUS, IT'S A NORMAL-TYPE POKÉMON WHO DOESN'T HAVE MANY WEAKNESS-ES. BUT...

SURE, THAT SLAKING WAS STRONG ...

OH, THAT? YOU DON'T UNDERSTAND, DO YOU?

I CAN'T BELIEVE YOU TRADED THAT POWERFUL SLAKING AWAY!

YOU NEED TO CONSIDER THE ORDER AND ROLE.

THAT'S RIGHT. I DIDN'T WANT SLAKING UP FRONT.

TA-DAH

... "ORDER AND ROLE"?

THE SECOND POKÉMON ON A TEAM IS THE **LEAD FIGHTER.**

I WANT A SWIFT POKÉMON FOR THAT, SO I CAN ATTACK RAPID-FIRE WHILE I'VE GOT THE CHANCE.

THE FIRST POKÉMON HAS THE ROLE OF **VAN-GUARD.**

FOR THAT ROLE, I USUALLY CHOOSE A POKÉMON WHO CAN USE A LOT OF DIFFERENT TYPES OF MOVES— OR ONE WHO CAN WITHSTAND OPPO-NENTS WHO USE SPECIAL MOVES.

SMASH

BATTLE 3, 5TH SET (31 BATTLES IN A ROW)!

LINOONE, FRUSTRATION!

BATTLE 4 (32 BATTLES IN A ROW)!

BATTLE 5 (33 BATTLES IN A ROW)!

BATTLE 6 (34 BATTLES IN A ROW)!

AND ALSO... FRUSTRATION IS A MOVE THAT DEALS MORE DAMAGE THE LOWER THE FRIENDSHIP BETWEEN THE POKÉMON AND TRAINER...MAKING IT THE **PERFECT** MOVE TO USE WITH A RENTAL POKÉMON!

LINOONE IS A NORMAL-TYPE POKÉMON WHO ENHANCES THE POWER OF THAT MOVE...

FRUSTRA-TION IS A NORMAL-TYPE MOVE.

THAT LINOONE IS DOING VERY WELL!

HE'S RIGHT!

WHO DID EMERALD CHOOSE ?!

WOM SWISH

HEAL DAMAGE AND MY LAST POKÉMON TRADE...

...NO REWARD ....?

No

Risk

No

Reward

WHAT'S THAT MEAN?!

JUMP

KRNCH

FFF

THIS MEANS THAT NOLAND IS WILLING TO TAKE BIG RISKS IN ORDER TO ACHIEVE VICTORY IN BATTLE!

NOW I GET IT...!

IT'S AN EXTREMELY POWERFUL BUT RISKY MOVE. THE OPPONENT GETS TO MOVE FIRST, BUT IF YOUR POKÉMON IS ATTACKED BEFORE IT USES THE MOVE, THE MOVE IS CANCELED OUT!

FOCUS PUNCH!

SWITCH OUT!

THAT LINOONE LOOKS LIKE IT'S ABOUT TO FAINT...

BUT I CAN'T ALLOW IT TO USE FRUS-TRATION BEFORE IT FAINTS.

I'LL USE IRON DEFENSE TO BE DOUBLE SURE!

PINSIR!

MAWILE, FLAME-THROWER! HEH... MAWILE HAS A POWERFUL ADVANTAGE AGAINST BUG-TYPES!

THAT LOOKS LIKE A VERY STRONG POKÉMON.

BUT THE MAWILE ON MY TEAM HAS A WELL-BALANCED VARIETY OF MOVES.

URP

IS THAT...?

WHAT ARE YOU DOING? I SAID FLAMETHROWER, NOT IRON DEFENSE!

COULD IT BE...?!

AN ITEM THAT FORCES A POKÉMON TO ONLY USE ONE MOVE. WHY IS MY MAWILE HOLDING THAT...?

IT IS!

CHOICE BAND

LUM BERRY

THAT'S RIGHT. I USED TRICK TO SWITCH THE ITEMS THE POKÉMON WERE HOLDING.

MY LINOONE USED IT RIGHT BEFORE I SWITCHED IT WITH PINSIR. THEN I SWAPPED THE CHOICE BAND WITH MAWILE'S LUM BERRY.

A CHOICE BAND?!

HE KNOCKED PINSIR OUT BY ATTACKING ITS WEAKNESS!

A ROCK-TYPE MOVE AGAINST PINSIR!

LINOONE AGAIN!

DIG!

AT THIS POINT, IT'S IMPOSSIBLE FOR ME TO LOSE!

YOUR LINOONE CAN BARELY STAND AFTER ITS FIGHT WITH MAWILE...

IT'S POINTLESS TO GO ON!

IT WAS A POWERFUL POKÉMON WITH GOOD MOVES, TO BE SURE...

HA! YOU MUST HAVE THOUGHT YOU'D WON THIS BATTLE AFTER YOU CALLED OUT PINSIR.

BUT...

● FAINTED ●

Linoone ♂	Normal
Ability: Pickup	
● Trick	● Frustration
● Dig	● Thunder Wave

m Berry

EMERALD ONLY HAS ONE MORE POKÉMON LEFT...!

DOUBLE-EDGE!

...EVEN A POWERFUL POKÉMON LIKE THAT CAN BE QUICKLY DEFEATED DURING THE COURSE OF BATTLE.

THAT'S WHAT MAKES POKÉMON BATTLES SO EXCITING!

THIS IS THE KNOWL-EDGE SYMBOL...

...AN HONOR BESTOWED UPON THOSE WHO BEAT FACTORY HEAD NOLAND AT THE BATTLE FACTORY IN THE TEST OF KNOWLEDGE!

THIS BATTLE IS ONLY A DEMON-STRATION...

...BUT I WILL OFFICIALLY GIVE THIS TO YOU IF YOU MANAGE TO DEFEAT ME.

NOW SHOW ME WHAT YOU KNOW!

HOW WILL YOU FACE ME WITH THE THIRD POKÉMON YOU TRADED FOR AT THE VERY END...?!

DEAR MEMBERS OF THE PRESS...

Thank you for visiting my Battle Frontier today. Permit me to continue explaining the rules of this facility...

OWNER: SCOTT

■ IN CASE OF A DOUBLE KNOCKOUT ■

The result is a tie and a rematch will be arranged if the battle is between two regular Trainers. If the battle was against a Frontier Brain, the Brain is the winner.

■ BATTLE POINTS ■

The accumulation of Battle Points corresponds with your results at each facility. Collected Battle Points may be exchanged for items at the Battle Point Exchange Service Corner.

FACILITY RULES	Battle-type	Number of Pokémon	Type of Symbol	Wins needed to attain the Symbol
BATTLE FACTORY	Single	3 Pokémon	Knowledge	7 Battles × 6 Sets = 42 Consecutive Wins
	Double	3 Pokémon		

Battle Factory battles are fought using rental Pokémon. The challenger chooses three out of six randomly selected Pokémon. If the challenger wins, they have the option of exchanging one of their Pokémon for one of their opponent's Pokémon. The newly acquired Pokémon takes the same position in the group as the one that was traded away.

Factory Head Noland   Knowledge Symbol

◆307◆

Gotcha Where
I Wantcha, Glalie

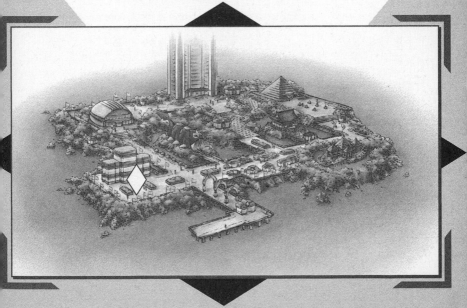

NOW! THE DUST HAS SET- TLED!

HUH ?!

GLARE

I DON'T KNOW WHAT YOU'RE UP TO, BUT YOU CAN'T DEFEAT THE FACTORY HEAD USING PARLOR TRICKS!

THAT SINISTER LOOK HAS DISAP- PEARED FROM SCEP- TILE'S EYES!

I KNOW!

...

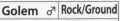

YEAH!

GLALIE IS A GRASS-TYPE POKÉMON'S GREATEST ENEMY— AN ICE-TYPE POKÉMON!

NOLAND'S THIRD POKÉMON IS GLALIE!

AHHH!

...IS FREEZING SCEPTILE'S BODY!

AND THE CHILL FROM GLALIE...

FSSSS

CRUNCH!

 BUT LET'S SEE HOW LONG THAT'LL LAST... AHAHA HA...

IT USED LEFTOVERS TO HEAL ITSELF...

EVEN AN AMATEUR LIKE ME CAN TELL THAT NOLAND WON'T STOP AT THAT.

THE OTHER FRONTEIR BRAINS ARE RIGHT.

IT'S A POWERFUL MOVE THAT CAN KNOCK OUT ITS OPPONENT WITH A SINGLE HIT!

 ...SHEER COLD!

 THE MOVE WHICH NOLAND'S GLALIE COULD USE TO DEFEAT EMERALD IS...

WHAT ARE YOU GOING TO DO NOW, EMERALD?!

JUST AS I SUS- PEC- TED!

 NOLAND DIDN'T USE SHEER COLD RIGHT AWAY! HE'S ATTACKING WITH ICE BEAM FIRST!

THE LIKELI-HOOD OF DODGING AN ATTACK DECREASES IF IT'S USED OVER AND OVER.

BUT DETECT HAS ITS WEAK-NESS TOO!

I'D HAVE FAILED IF I'D STAKED EVERY-THING ON SHEER COLD.

 YOU'RE DODGING MY ATTACKS USING DETECT!

LOOKS LIKE YOU'RE OUT OF LUCK TODAY!

THIS SHOULD BE ABOUT THE RIGHT TIME...

SHEER COLD!

BOINK

SKRITCH

BOINK

UMPH

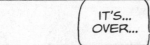

IT'S... OVER...

NOPE. THIS BATTLE ISN'T OVER YET.

RMMPPH

YOU THINK SO...?

THE BATTLE IS OVER!

OR DID YOU SOME- HOW DODGE IT?!

IT... STOOD UP?! BUT IT RECEIVED A DIRECT HIT FROM THAT ATTACK!

GTMMP

WHAT'S THE MATTER, GLALIE?!

STGGR

!

I PLANTED THE SEED WHEN IT WAS BITING MY SCEPTILE.

IT FINALLY STARTED TO TAKE EFFECT.

THIS IS...

YOUR GLALIE WAS SLOWLY LOSING ITS STRENGTH AS WELL.

OKAY ...

ZOOMP

...LEECH SEED!

FWUMP

BLIP

6 SET 7 BATTLE

TOTAL 42 WIN

IMPOSSIBLE.

NO.

NO WAY.

WHAT?

GLALIE HAS FAINTED!!

AND EMERALD HAS WON!!

● FAINTED ●

Glalie ♂	Ice

Ability: Inner Focus
- Crunch
- Sheer Cold
- Ice Beam
- Rest

Held Item: Chesto Berry

HE WON!!

NOW WE CAN INTERVIEW THEM AND CALL IT A DAY.

FINALLY! IT'S OVER!

MAYBE I SHOULD HAVE HAD GOLEM USE EXPLOSION A LOT EARLIER?

I THOUGHT I CHOSE A PRETTY SOLID GROUP. WHERE DID I GO WRONG...?

OH, I SEE!

GLALIE'S CHESTO BERRY WAS MEANT TO BE USED TOGETHER WITH REST, SO......

SHOULDN'T YOU HAVE HAD AT LEAST ONE POKÉMON WITH LEFT-OVERS OR SHELL BELL?

POKÉ-MON ORDER ...

...ITEMS...

...THE MOVES...

NO...

BUT...

NAH... I DON'T KNOW ABOUT THAT. MAYBE YOU SHOULD HAVE MADE BETTER USE OF YOUR ITEMS...?

Um... Excuse us... Could you please grant us an interview now...?

WE'VE BEEN WAITING FOR 42 BATTLES, YOU KNOW! MORE THAN FIFTEEN HOURS!

WILL YOU GUYS CUT IT OUT ALREADY?!

WOW, CONGRAT- ULATIONS!

GEE, THANKS!

WHAT SECRET?

BY THE WAY, EMERALD... ISN'T IT ABOUT TIME YOU TOLD ME YOUR SECRET?

THAT SCEPTILE YOU USED AT THE END.

THE ARENA WAS COVERED IN DUST SO NOLAND AND THE OTHER FRONTIER BRAINS COULDN'T SEE...

...BUT I CAUGHT YOU ON CAMERA. YOU DID SOMETHING TO THAT SCEPTILE TO CALM IT DOWN!

HEY! YOU CAN'T TAKE THOSE POKÉMON WITH YOU!

FOR STARTERS, ABOUT THIS GUY...

STRETCH

I'LL TELL YOU EVERYTHING!

SURE!

WHY WOULD A RENTAL POKÉMON BE SO VIOLENT TO BEGIN WITH...?

...BUT YOU WEREN'T PAYING ATTENTION TO WHAT WAS GOING ON **BEFORE** IT ATTACKED ME, WERE YOU?

YOU WERE BRAGGING ABOUT HOW YOU TOOK THAT PHOTO...

CHECK **WHAT** OUT?!

'CAUSE I NEED TO CHECK IT OUT.

HOW SO?!

DON'T WORRY, IT'S OKAY.

THE REASON THIS SCEPTILE ATTACKED ME...

...IS BECAUSE SOMEONE IN THE AUDIENCE USED THE MOVE POISON STING ON IT!

TUCKER AND BRANDON ARE IN A HUFF BECAUSE NOLAND WAS DEFEATED!

THIS IS BAD, LUCY!

FINE. TELL THEM I'LL FACE THE BOY NEXT.

WHAT'S ALL THE FUSS ABOUT?

I'LL BE WAITING FOR YOU AT THE BATTLE PIKE...

...LITTLE BOY!

DEAR MEMBERS OF THE PRESS...

Thank you for visiting the Battle Frontier today. Permit me to continue explaining the rules of this facility...

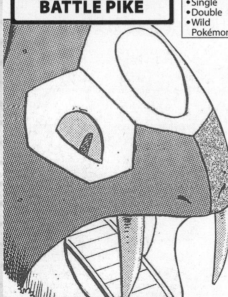

FACILITY RULES
BATTLE PIKE

Battle-type	Number of Pokémon	Type of Symbol	Wins needed to attain the Symbol
• Single • Double • Wild Pokémon	3 Pokémon	Luck	14 Rooms × 10 Sets = 140 Rooms

At this facility, you choose between three routes to travel until you reach the room at the very end. Eight possible events will occur inside each room. What you will encounter is determined at random.

A healing event, which heals the challenger's Pokémon, is included among the eight events.

There is also a Double Battle Event, but this will not occur if the challenger does not have two or more Pokémon capable of fighting.

Pike Queen Lucy

Luck Symbol

308

As Luck Would Have It, Kirlia

CAN YOU GET SCEPTILE OUT OF THE POKÉ BALL?

SURE!

WE'RE COMING, EM'!

FLAP

FLAP

FLAP

BOM

OKAY.

USE THE POKÉNAV TO DETERMINE SCEPTILE'S LEVEL.

TMP

I'VE NEVER SEEN THESE POKÉMON BEFORE. AND...

...THEY'RE "TALKING" TELEPATHI-CALLY TO EMERALD?!

Condition
Party PKMN

SCEPTILE ♂/Lv.51

COOL

TOUGH · BEAUTY

SMART · CUTE

IT'S LEVEL 51!

I CAN'T HEAR THEM, BUT FROM THE EXPRESSION ON THEIR FACES, IT CERTAINLY LOOKS LIKE THEY'RE HAVING A CON-VERSATION.

I DID IT, LATIAS, LATIOS!

THINK ABOUT IT... REMEMBER WHEN I GOT ATTACKED WITH SHEER COLD...?

BUT IT'S TRUE. IT'S 51. THERE'S NO MISTAKE ABOUT IT.

THERE CAN'T BE A POKÉMON WITH A DIFFERENT LEVEL!

LEVEL 51?! THAT'S IMPOSSIBLE! YOU CHOSE THE LEVEL 50 COURSE AT THE BATTLE FACTORY. THAT MEANS ALL THE RENTAL POKÉMON SHOULD BE LEVEL 50.

SHEER COLD!

NOPE. THIS BATTLE ISN'T OVER YET.

OR DID YOU SOMEHOW DODGE IT?!

IT... STOOD BUT IT RECEIVED A DIRECT HIT FROM THAT ATTACK!

RMMPD

YES... NOW I SEE...

BINGO!

BECAUSE ITS LEVEL WAS HIGHER!

SHEER COLD IS AN ATTACK THAT FAILS IF YOUR OPPONENT'S LEVEL IS HIGHER THAN YOURS.

SCEPTILE DIDN'T REPEL OR WITHSTAND THE ATTACK...

...YET IT WASN'T DEFEATED.

HMM...

SEE? NOW DO YOU BELIEVE THAT IT'S LEVEL 51?

EVEN IF NOLAND DELIBERATELY INCLUDED A HIGHER LEVEL POKÉMON IN THIS BATTLE, IT WOULDN'T MAKE SENSE FOR HIM TO LET EMERALD USE IT, SO... WHAT DOES THIS ALL ADD UP TO?!

OH. BUT NOLAND DIDN'T NOTICE ITS HIGHER LEVEL EITHER.

NOPE.

SO... YOU CHOSE SCEPTILE BECAUSE YOU KNEW IT WAS STRONGER THAN THE OTHERS?

DOME ACE TUCKER!

PYRAMID KING BRAN- DON!

NICE MIST BALL, LATIAS!

WHAT'S THIS? SOME SORT OF MIST SURROUNDING THOSE THREE... I CAN'T SEE THEM!

FSSS

HUH ?

DON'T WORRY... LOOK!

OH NO! THIS ISN'T GOOD! IF THEY FIND OUT YOU TOOK THE SCEPTILE FROM THE BATTLE FACTORY...

116

AHHH! IT FELL OFF AGAIN!

SNAP

FOUND YOU AT LAST, YOU LITTLE RUNT!

DON'T CALL ME A RUNT!

STOP IT, TUCKER. DON'T BE SO CHILDISH.

SEE? YOU ARE A RUNT!

THAT INCOMPETENT COBBLER...

THANKS!

EMERALD, IS IT? I'M IMPRESSED BY HOW WELL YOU CONTROLLED YOUR POKÉMON DURING YOUR BATTLE AGAINST NOLAND.

I'M SLEEPY. COULD YOU JUST TELL ME WHAT YOU'RE HERE FOR?

OW.

WHAT'S YOUR POINT...?

GRRR

RIGHT. DON'T THINK THAT.

BUT DON'T THINK YOU CAN GET THROUGH **EVERY** FACILITY LIKE THAT.

OR MY BATTLE PYRAMID?!

WE'RE HERE TO ASK WHICH ONE OF US YOU PLAN TO CHALLENGE TOMORROW!

MY BATTLE DOME?!

BUT I HAVEN'T CONSIDERING CHALLENG-ING EITHER OF YOU YET BECAUSE...

HMM... I'M GOING TO BE CHALLENGING ALL THE FACILITIES IN THE END, SO I DON'T CARE WHICH ONE I DO NEXT.

...YOU GUYS!!

...I DON'T LIKE...

WAKE
UP!

...NNN...

HEY!
DON'T
GO TO
SLEEP!
UNTIE
US!

OH
WELL...
IT'S LATE
ANYWAY
AND I'M
TIRED.
GUESS
I'LL JUST
SLEEP
HERE
LIKE THIS.
YAWN...

DO
SOME-
THING!

HEY!
WE'RE
BOUND
TO
SOME-
THING!
WE CAN'T
MOVE!

MAKE UP
YOUR MIND!
YOU JUST
TOLD ME
NOT TO
MOVE!

I HOPE
TUCKER AND
BRANDON
HAVEN'T
CAUGHT HIM...

EMERALD
WENT OFF
SOMEWHERE
AFTER THAT,
BUT WHERE...?

HUH
?

WHAT
AM I
SUP-
POSED
TO DO
WITH
THIS
SCEP-
TILE?

THOSE TWO
POKÉMON
CALLED
LATIOS AND
LATIAS FLEW
BACK UP INTO
THE SKY...

UM...

ZZZZ...

POISON TAIL!

WHAT'S GOING ON?!

SLASH

TUCKER... BRANDON...

TALK ABOUT PITIFUL.

WHOA!

KAFUMP!

OOF!

SIGH...

...PRETTY LUCKY ...DON'T YOU THINK?

...THEN HE'S...

IF THIS BOY ESCAPED INTO THE BATTLE FRONTIER AND CAME TO THE BATTLE PIKE BY PURE COINCI- DENCE...

SURE!

WHAT DO YOU SAY? WOULD YOU LIKE TO CHALLENGE THE BATTLE PIKE AND TEST YOUR LUCK TODAY? HMM?

ALLOW ME TO INTRODUCE MYSELF AGAIN.

I'M LUCY...

...THE PIKE QUEEN.

THE KIND OF EVENT YOU FACE IS TOTALLY UP TO LUCK—RANDOM CHANCE, IN OTHER WORDS.

...WHERE YOU'LL EXPERIENCE EIGHT KINDS OF EVENTS SUCH AS BATTLES AND HEALING FOR YOUR POKÉMON.

THERE ARE SMALLER ROOMS BEHIND THOSE THREE DOORS...

YOU MUST CHOOSE ONE OF THE DOORS IN THE LARGE ROOM TO GO THROUGH. EVENTUALLY YOU'LL REACH THE ROOM AT THE VERY END.

THE BATTLE PIKE IS A FACILITY THAT'S ALL ABOUT LUCK.

THE CHALLENGER ENTERS THE FACILITY WITH THREE POKÉMON.

..IF YOU MAKE IT TO THE END OF THE 10TH SET... AFTER GETTING THROUGH THE 139TH ROOM!

YOU'RE ONLY ALLOWED TO FACE ME...

THERE ARE SEVEN LARGE ROOMS AND SEVEN SMALL ROOMS. FOURTEEN ROOMS IN ALL MAKE UP A SET.

LARGE ROOM 10

SMALL ROOM ×

SMALL ROOM ×

SMALL ROOM

LARGE ROOM 9 ×

SMALL ROOM ×

SMALL ROOM

SMALL ROOM ×

LARGE RO

...JUST LIKE IN NOLAND'S BATTLE FACILITY.

AND NO MATTER HOW FAR YOU GET, YOU'LL HAVE TO START FROM SCRATCH AGAIN IF ALL YOUR POKÉMON ARE DEFEATED...

OKAY! JUST HOLD ON A MINUTE! I'LL BE READY SOON!

HELLO, EMER-ALD.

I'LL ACCEPT YOUR CHAL-LENGE ANY TIME!

TELL ME WHEN YOU'RE READY!

LOOKS LIKE THE PRESS HAVE ARRIVED...

MURMUR

MURMUR

THE BATTLE PIKE DOESN'T HAVE RENTAL POKÉMON LIKE THE BATTLE FACTORY. YOU HAVE TO USE YOUR OWN POKÉMON!

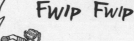

FWIP FWIP

YOU MEAN "READY" AS IN... YOU'RE GOING TO PREPARE THREE POKÉMON? HOW ARE YOU GOING TO ACCOMPLISH THAT?

BUT I THOUGHT YOU SAID YOU DIDN'T HAVE ANY POKÉMON OF YOUR OWN!

DIFFERENT...

SO YOU'RE GOING TO USE SCEPTILE AND THOSE POKÉMON FROM YESTERDAY, LATIAS AND LATIOS?

I KNOW!

BUT...

I DON'T.

NAH... I'M THINKING ABOUT USING DIFFERENT POKÉMON.

...AND SHE TOLD ME I CAN USE WHICHEVER ONES I WANT WHENEVER I WANT!

...THE PERSON WHO SENT ME TO THE BATTLE FRONTIER HAS **EVERY** POKÉMON...

THE PERSON... WHO SENT YOU TO... THE BATTLE FRONTIER ?!

PC SERVICE ...START! ...

KLKK KLKK KLKK

THAT'S RIGHT.

WELL, THEN ...

POKÉMON RESEARCH CENTER 3RD HOENN BRANCH LAB

UH-HUH... UH-HUH...

OH, IT'S EMERALD!

OKAY!

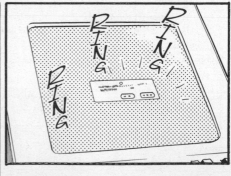

RING RING RING

A DOUBLE BATTLE AGAINST VIRTUAL TRAINERS!

LOOK OUT, EMERALD!

FWEEEEE

OO OH

W

THAT ATTACK WILL INFLICT A STATUS CONDITION ON YOUR POKÉMON!

TO BE CONTINUED...

EMERALD

HIS CLOTHES, HAIRDO, PLATFORM SHOES... WHAT A— ERR— UNIQUE LOOK HE HAS. ACTUALLY, IT STRUCK ME AS KIND OF **WEIRD** THE FIRST TIME I SAW HIM. HE DOESN'T SEEM TO BE HIDING ANYTHING, AND HE'LL ANSWER ANYTHING I ASK HIM... BUT HIS MYSTIQUE ONLY CONTINUES TO GROW... I'LL KEEP AFTER HIM UNTIL I GET THE FULL SCOOP!

- Birthplace: Unknown (Somewhere in the Hoenn region)
- Birthday: May 31
- Blood-type: AB (RH Negative)
- Age: 11 Years Old (As of Adventure 308)
- Hobby: Pokémon Battle
- Pokémon Owned: None!

THIS IS ALL THE DATA I'VE GATHERED ON HIM SO FAR.

■POKÉDEX■

HE CHECKS POKÉMON DATA WITH THIS DEVICE.
I'VE NEVER SEEN ONE BEFORE AND I DON'T KNOW
WHO CREATED IT OR WHERE IT WAS MADE.

■E SHOOTER■

HE SHOOTS CALMING PELLETS OUT OF THIS
DEVICE. THE POKÉMON TARGETED BY THE
PELLETS CALMS DOWN RIGHT AWAY. BUT WHY?

■POKÉNAV■

A MUST-HAVE TOOL FOR ALL HOENN TRAINERS.
THE TRAINERS PARTICIPATING IN THE BATTLE
FRONTIER USE IT TO CHECK THEIR POKÉMON'S
CONDITION, AMONG OTHER THINGS.

■FRONTIER PASS■

THIS CERTIFIES YOU AS A BATTLE FRONTIER
CHALLENGER. EMERALD HAS ONE AND STORES
THE SYMBOLS (THE BATTLE FRONTIER EQUIVA-
LENT OF GYM BADGES) THAT HE WINS INSIDE IT.

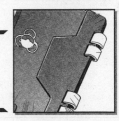

■MECHANICAL HANDS■

MECHANICAL ARMS THAT STRETCH OUT FROM HIS
SLEEVES. I HAVEN'T HAD A CHANCE TO LOOK UP
HIS SLEEVES. WHERE ARE HIS REAL ARMS?

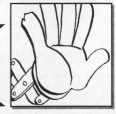

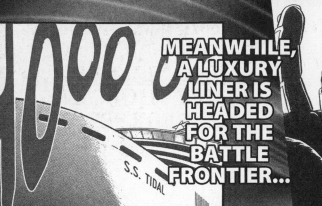

MEANWHILE, A LUXURY LINER IS HEADED FOR THE BATTLE FRONTIER...

S.S. TIDAL

THE STAR THAT WILL MAKE MY WISH COME TRUE. COME TO ME!

HONORARY CAPTAIN, MR. BRINEY! WHAT ARE THESE?

STATUES. THERE ARE FIVE OF THEM.

WE'RE GONNA MOVE 'EM IN TO THE BATTLE TOWER AFTER THE WEDDING TOMORROW....

COME TO GUILE!

POKéMON

EMERALD

ONE MAN STANDS IN THE WAY OF EMERALD AND THE FRONTIER BRAINS ATTEMPT TO CAPTURE JIRACHI...

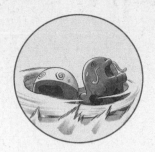

Message from
Hidenori Kusaka

I've received the answers to a survey I placed in vol. 23.* This survey was designed so I could get to know more about you, our readers. I asked how old you are and how many volumes of the Pokémon Adventures series you own. I like to analyze things, so I really enjoyed crunching the data from the survey—such as the range of readers' ages, who reads the series in serialized form in magazines as opposed to who reads it after it's compiled into graphic novels, etc. I'm working hard to use this data to improve the comic. I'd like to thank everyone who helped out by taking the survey!

*In the original Japanese edition.

Message from
Satoshi Yamamoto

The main concept behind the new battleground called the Battle Frontier is to show how fun and complex a Pokémon Battle can be. How will Emerald defeat the Frontier Brains, who fight using a variety of strategies, unlike Gym Leaders, who mostly strategize along the lines of the Pokémon's type?

More Adventures Coming Soon...

When a mysterious armored person in search of the Wish Pokémon Jirachi attacks Nolan, Emerald is the prime suspect! Jirachi grants wishes, but only awakens every one thousand years for seven days.

How can Emerald and the Frontier Brains prevent Jirachi's power from falling into the wrong hands?!

AVAILABLE MARCH 2015!

Take a trip with Pokémon

ALL THAT PIKACHU!
ANI-MANGA™

Meet Pikachu and
all-star Pokémon!
Two complete Pikachu
stories taken from the
Pokémon movies—all in
a full color manga.

Buy yours today!

POKÉMON

www.pokemon.com

vizkids

VIZ media
www.viz.com

The Struggle for Time and Space Begins Again!

Pokémon Trainer Ash and his Pikachu must find the Jewel of Life and stop Arceus from devastating all existence! The journey will be both dangerous and uncertain: even if Ash and his friends can set an old wrong right again, will there be time to return the Jewel of Life before Arceus destroys everything and everyone they've ever known?

Manga edition also available from VIZ Media

POKÉMON
ARCEUS
JEWEL OF LIFE
A TALE UNTOLD. A LEGEND UNLEASHED.

POKÉMON
ARCEUS
AND THE
JEWEL OF LIFE

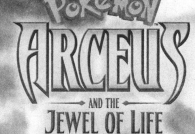

THIS IS THE END OF
THIS GRAPHIC NOVEL!

To properly enjoy this VIZ Media
graphic novel, please turn it around
and begin reading from right to left.

This book has been printed in the
original Japanese format in order
to preserve the orientation of the
original artwork.

Have fun with it!

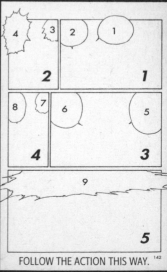